Woza Friday

Library Learning Information

Idea Store® Bow
1 Gladstone Place
Roman Road
London E3 5ES

020 7364 4332

Created and managed by
Tower Hamlets Council

THE NEW READERS PROJECT

The New Readers Project of the Department of Adult and Community Education, University of Natal, Durban develops and supports adult literacy and basic English Second Language skills by producing books in simple language for the entertainment and education of adults. Each of the books has been evaluated and modified by potential readers.

The project was set up with funding from the Canadian Embassy; The Chairman's Fund Educational Trust; Development and Peace; The Hexagon Trust; The Energos Foundation; Rockefeller Brothers Fund and the Trust for Educational Advancement in South Africa.

About this book

This book was written in response to a request from Jojilanga Adult Education Centre, Umlazi.

Thanks

We thank the following people for their help in evaluating this book:

DP Majola, SM Mkhize, Phineas Mthembu, Malan Zondi and TC Zwane from the Spar Natal English Group;

Dokotela Dladla, Elphas Madonda, Cyprian Sokhela and Romy Ward from Umgeni Water English Group;

Jean Dyson and the English learners group at the Scottsville Presbyterian Church in Pietermaritzburg.

How to contact us

If you want to know more about the New Readers Project or find out about other books which we publish, please contact:

Dept. of Adult and Community Education
University of Natal
Durban
4041
South Africa

On Monday
when I wake up

2

my head is sore

4

my tongue is thick

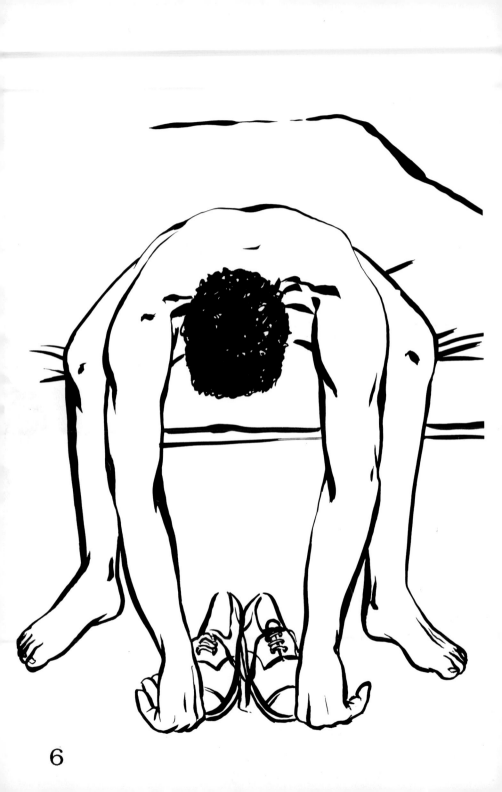

6

my arms are heavy

7

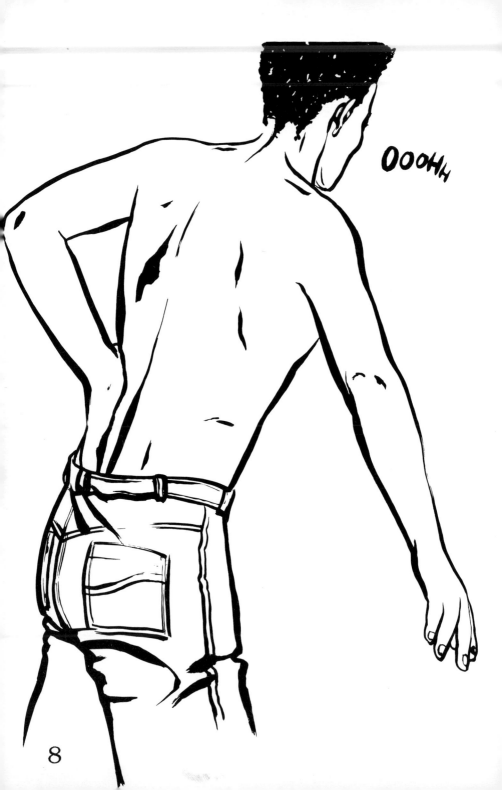

my back hurts

10

my legs are slow

I can hardly move.

14

But on Friday
when I wake up

16

my eyes are bright

18

my heart is light

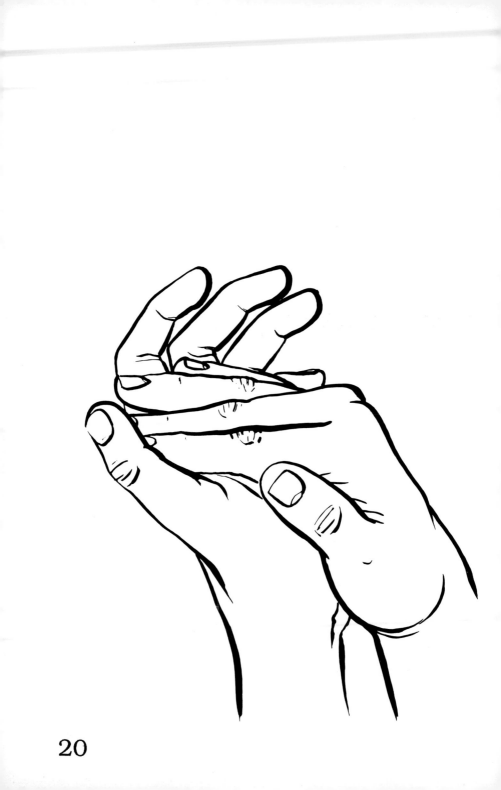

my hands clap

22

my fingers snap

my feet tap

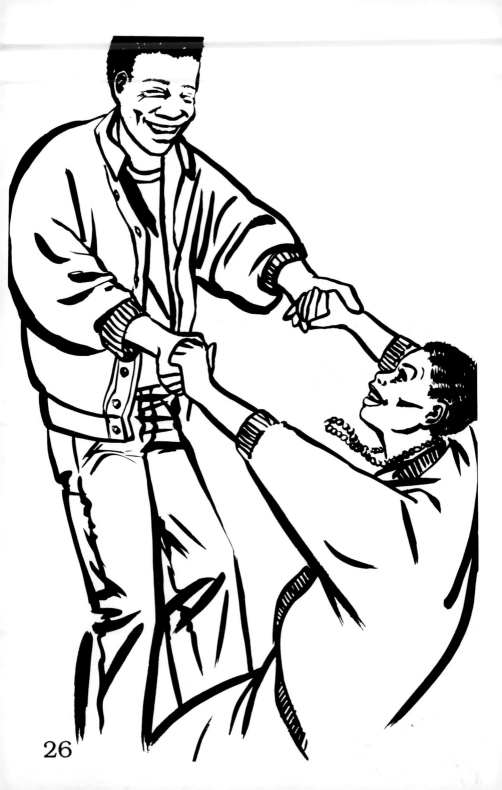

I am ready for the
weekend.

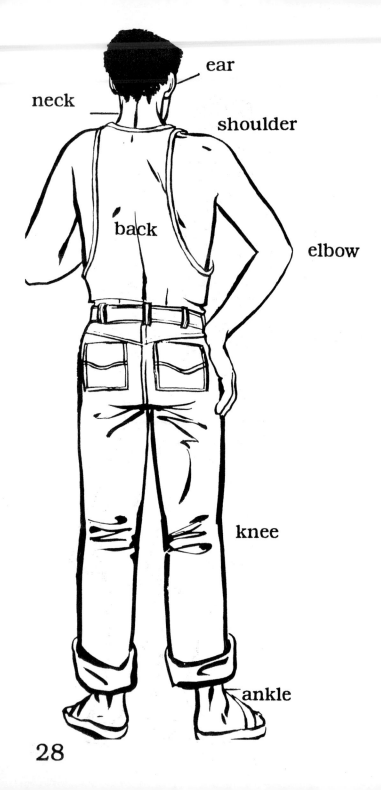

ear

neck

shoulder

back

elbow

knee

ankle

28

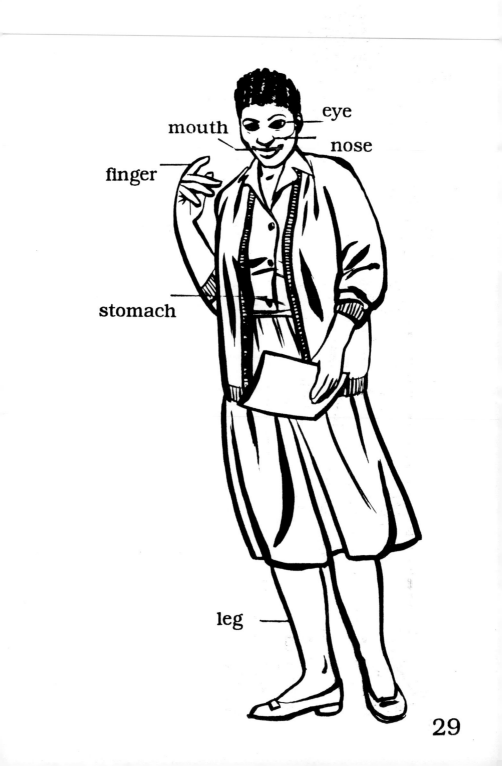

mouth

eye

nose

finger

stomach

leg

29